PRAISE FOR

THE YELLOW HOUSE ON THE LEFT

"Chelsea told me she was an old soul in a young body. Her honest, brave and pull-no-punches story about her battle with cancer proves this and every story in this book is a lesson to us all. From Chelsea I've learned to live and love more fully, as if it was your last day, because you truly never know when that might be. BIG love to you and all whose lives you continue to touch. Let's take the scenic route."

—KAY WHITE, *kaywhite.com*

"A brave and beautiful book about making the most of every moment, even when those moments are few. Chelsea's story will touch your heart and change the way you look at life, death, and above all, love."

—LISA CANFIELD, *copycoachlisa.com*

"Chelsea's real, honest and brave account will remind you to savor each day and appreciate all that you have. It's full of love, sorrow and a whole lot of inspiration. The grace and selflessness in which she has handled her life's journey and now her final act is nothing short of amazing."

—LISA BJORNSON *solamaragency.com*

"To the jaded or cynical among us—I challenge you to read about Chelsea's journey towards the end, the way she has transformed her own tragedy into a multitude of joy for others, and not have your faith in humanity restored. "

—SAM GEORGE *solamaragency.com*

"Like your dearest friendship, Chelsea's story will pull you into life's beautiful embrace. Her love of life and her raw honesty will awaken you to the inherent wholeness of your own story too—your joys and sorrows, your fears and con-solations, and most of all, the profound love that connects us all. She has changed me, forever."

—PAUL SIGAFUS, *coloradocounselingcenter.com*

"Chelsea has left us one last gift. Her dying words are a beacon shedding light, comfort and hope to anyone walking through grief. "

—EMILY GARMAN, *thesocialanimal.com*

"This story touched my heart, inspired me, and made me want to savor every single moment of life. I couldn't be more happy that Chelsea has decided to share her story that until now very few knew. Buckle up and enjoy the journey."

—SHAWN SHEPHEARD, *shawnshepheard.com*

"A book of wisdom, compassion, and piercing honesty."

—TAMARA GOLD, *tamaragold.com*

"This is the perfect book on how we emerge from suffering and challenge with real, encompassing wisdom and love. Full of personal growth and emotional fulfillment."

—MIKE FLANNERY, *stopunderachievingnow.com*

"A powerful story of loss, love and redemption that will stir the souls of its readers and remind you you're not alone."

—GABRIELLE BERNSTEIN, *gabbybernstein.com*

The

YELLOW HOUSE ON THE LEFT

The

YELLOW HOUSE ON THE LEFT

What Dying Young is Teaching Me About Living

CHELSEA BERLER

Published in Santa Rosa Beach, Florida, USA by Chelsea Berler.
Printed at Cedar Graphics, Davenport, Iowa, USA.
mostlychelsea.com

ISBN-13: 978-0-692-11072-0
ISBN-10: 0-692-11072-0

Author Contact
Chelsea Berler // Foye Belle Foundation, Inc.
174 Watercolor Way
Suite 103-420
Santa Rosa Beach, FL 32459
800-780-8388
hello@mostlychelsea.com

Book cover design by Jill Anderson @ solamaragency.com
Layout design by Sam George @ solamaragency.com
Author photograph by Siddiqi Ray @ siddiqisoulray.com

First Edition

"Here Comes the Sun" by The Beatles

Here comes the sun (doo doo doo doo)
Here comes the sun, and I say
It's all right

Little darling, it's been a long cold lonely winter
Little darling, it feels like years since it's been here
Here comes the sun
Here comes the sun, and I say
It's all right

Little darling, the smiles returning to the faces
Little darling, it seems like years since it's been here
Here comes the sun
Here comes the sun, and I say
It's all right

Sun, sun, sun, here it comes
Sun, sun, sun, here it comes
Sun, sun, sun, here it comes
Sun, sun, sun, here it comes
Sun, sun, sun, here it comes

Little darling, I feel that ice is slowly melting
Little darling, it seems like years since it's been clear
Here comes the sun
Here comes the sun, and I say
It's all right

Here comes the sun
Here comes the sun, and I say
It's all right
It's all right

(I hope you're singing or humming this, Mom! I love you!)

CONTENTS

HOME IS WHERE THE HEART IS

"Alice: How long is forever?
White Rabbit: Sometimes,
just one second."

–LEWIS CARROL, *ALICE IN WONDERLAND*

It all started with 30A.

30A is where we, meaning my husband Mark, our two rescue pups and I, live now. It's where our story started and where I now know our story, or at least my part of it, is going to end. But let's not get into that just yet...

30A is kind of a secret. It's not as famous as other Florida hot spots like Miami or Orlando, but it's still a destination for so many people. If you haven't been lucky enough to experience it, I can't recommend it enough. It's paradise. No, better than paradise. It's home.

Actually, technically, 30A is a road. Its official name is Florida Scenic Highway 30A, and it consists of a 19 to 24-mile stretch (depending on which authority you consult) of what's basically a country road in Northwest Florida, running east to west across this tiny stretch of the Panhandle between Destin and Panama City. The Gulf of Mexico is on one side and Choctawhatchee Bay is on the other, along with forests and sand dunes full of freshwater lakes and other bits of wonderfulness. The whole place is like a picture postcard—white sand, clear, blue-green water, funky shops, great restaurants and warm and welcoming people everywhere you go.

This message has been brought to you by the 30A Tourism Board.

Just kidding. But seriously, it's awesome.

30A was just a string of sleepy beach towns until the late '70s and early '80s, when it became famous for an architectural movement called New Urbanism. Conceived as an antidote to soulless suburban sprawl, New Urbanism was all about consciously designing communities to be more like small towns used to be—totally walkable, with town squares meant for gathering and sidewalks meant for meandering. The first of these communities, Seaside, was built in 1979, and its pastel houses with their big front porches and white picket fences were so perfectly picture-perfect, the town was the setting for the movie *The Truman Show*. It's just down the street from me—how rad is that? Lots of other communities, each with their own distinct personality and architectural style followed, from Charleston-styled Rosemary Beach to Mediterranean-themed Alys Beach, joining the older, established beach towns like Grayton Beach and Dune Allen Beach to form this incredibly special place.

However, the fact that I was living in paradise had pretty much escaped me the day I met Mark. I was a newcomer to 30A, having spontaneously decided to move to Florida from North Dakota, which is where I'm from and where my entire family lived. I was feeling especially lonely and blue that day and was complaining about it on the phone to my amazing mom, who basically ordered me to take a shower, shave my legs, get dressed and get out of the house.

It took her two tries. But lucky for me, I complied.

I went to a beachfront restaurant called Bud and Alley's, where I spotted a man at the bar who looked, if it was possible, even more down in the dumps than I was. I walked up to him and started a conversation during which I lied about watching football (I didn't and still don't and found out he didn't either!). Nine years later, I guess you could say that conversation is still going on.

I've written the whole story of how Mark and I got together in a previous book (it's called *The Curious One* if you are curious enough to want to know everything about me), so I won't go into too much detail. The short version is, we got married (on 30A of course – and at Bud and Alley's to boot!) and I moved to Birmingham, Alabama, where Mark, who is divorced, lived to be close to his two kids, Allison and Matt. We had a little vacation bungalow on 30A, which we tried to visit as often as we could, and life was good. Really good.

Then, about three years ago, I noticed that life was changing. Allison had already moved away. Matt was graduating from high school and heading out of state to college too. And since the only reason we were ever *in* Birmingham was to be there for Mark's kids (we both work remotely and travel a lot so we could basically live anywhere) and those kids were no longer there, I started wondering. Could we live at the beach full time?

I told Mark the idea and he thought I was crazy. He doesn't like change and couldn't really wrap his head around the idea of leaving Birmingham because it was all he'd known since the kids were little and he wanted to make sure he was always there for his kids should they come "home" to Birmingham. How could he leave that? Leave their memories, their home, their everything—it wasn't something he could get into his head. But he asked both Matt and Allison, and they were like, "MOVE TO THE BEACH! We'll visit you more there!"

Ha! We had their blessing… and that was everything to us. It mattered so much, and I think it also put Mark at ease with the idea too. At least at ease enough where we could start to talk about it.

But to really convince Mark, I knew I needed to be able to show him what our life at the beach would look like (did I mention he doesn't like change?) so he could see us in it. That meant I needed to find a home. We couldn't live in our beach bungalow. It was really small, no garage, and since my husband has 17 motorcycles—for real!—we definitely needed one of those. The beach bungalow was great, but it was a vacation home. I had to find us a *home* home.

That's when the yellow house on the left happened. That's when it all happened.

I found the house online and told Mark we needed to go look at it. Not that it would have been Mark's dream house under any circumstance. It was an *old* house that needed a very large hug. Mark had never lived in anything old; he always had new houses, new construction, new, shiny, clean everything. I, on the other hand, turned my nose up at new construction. There's something I love about an older house—how it needs love, life, breath. This house certainly fit those parameters.

I remember when we pulled up, I knew. *This is the one.* But to get Mark on board, it took a lot of convincing. A *lot* of convincing. Still, he finally saw it too. Or at least he saw how giddy it made me, how many ideas I had for it and all the projects I had planned for it (he was overwhelmed but I was definitely not!). So, we did it.

And let me tell you...that house is *still* a work in progress. We've dumped so much dang money into it. I realize now, old houses are really expensive! But so damn worth it. At least, this one has been. It's been my heart and soul.

And now, three years later, we wouldn't want to be anywhere else. We love it here. It's home. The garden is my favorite. We've made it so amazing, with citrus groves in our backyard amongst several different gardens I planted. We've also remodeled a lot. We even installed a yoga room in the tower!

I should tell you that normally I'm not a person who cares a lot about material things. I grew up poor and never had much. But I also grew up knowing how important a *home* is. How to make a home, how to love a home and how to be a home. And this home is all of that. A home is much more than a place to hang your hat for me; a home is just everything.

This home is everything.

And I'm going to miss it so much.

Because just when you think you're going to spend the rest of your life making a home, life happens. Or, in my case, the end of life happens. Or is happening. Way, way sooner than I ever expected. I'm only 34 as I write this. And I know that at some point I'm going have to say goodbye to it all. To this life Mark and I decided to make here on 30A, in this home, together. It will be just him and our rescue dogs. I feel awful for leaving him here, but I'm going to continue to make it a home for him, continue to do what I can until I can't—for him.

And also, for me. Because I love this life so much. It's going to be hard to let it go.

And that brings me to this book. To be honest, I'm not 100% sure why I'm writing it, except that it hit me like a bolt of lightning at 3am a few days ago when I was lying in bed buzzing from the steroids the doctors have me on. I had started writing about my "cancer journey" when I never doubted I'd beat my disease and come out just fine—those pieces are included in this book—and wrote again in a Facebook post (also included) when I learned that wasn't the case. I wanted all the people who were worried about me and praying for me and sending me all their love to understand how it all came out.

But my story's not over yet. And as a person looking at life from a perspective most 34-year-olds will never experience, maybe I have something to say that other people will find valuable. Maybe there are some nuggets of beauty in all this random awfulness that I can leave behind. Maybe I can make someone feel less afraid or appreciate what they have or inspire someone in some way.

After all, you only get one life. I've tried to make the most of mine. I hope you do the same with yours.

Chapter I

A SUMMER OF CHANGE

May, 2017

For about a year, we'd been living a lifestyle most people would consider seriously crazy. Mark was working in Europe. He went every single week and worked in Paris and London and flew home to me and the yellow house every weekend. Like I said, crazy.

I had never been to Europe. I traveled all over the States on my own before I met Mark, when I was building my business and getting my first taste of success and freedom and all that fun stuff. Mark and I have done pretty much everything in the Caribbean. Our first trip was to Curacao and we've been back multiple times and visited most of the other islands too. Costa Rica was another EPIC trip that we took that we loved. Oh, and Panama! That was amazing too!

Through all that, we'd never gotten to Europe together. But last year, with Mark working over there so much, we knew it was going to happen. We just wanted to plan the trip so we could really enjoy being together. Mark wanted to show me his life there, where he worked, how his days went and all that stuff I never got to experience.

Then, suddenly, the perfect time appeared on the horizon. There was this big MotoGP race (Grand Prix motorcycle racing) at Le Mans in France coming up that we both really wanted to experience. We're both big MotoGP fans. We've been to all the US races many, many times over since we met in 2009, but we'd never been to a race overseas and I hear they are as EPIC is they come. They know how to do it right.

So, we ended up planning the trip around that. And, OMG I was SO EXCITED to go. I hadn't really been "abroad" before...at least not what I considered "abroad," so this trip was a huge deal.

It turned out to be my favorite trip ever. The UK was fun, but I loved Paris! It was everything I thought of and more...just magical. We didn't go up the Eiffel Tower but we went there and walked around Paris and ate and drank a bunch. THE FOOD WAS THE BEST! Le Mans was EPIC—Mark got us VIP tickets and special passes, so we went all out! But the best part was just to be with Mark and live in his world for a while. And the VIP treatment wasn't bad either!

When we got home to the yellow house on the left, we had big plans. Mark had been banking all his hotel points and flight points so we could head back to Europe. We wanted to get to Greece and the Greek Islands and really drink in life. At the same time, we also wanted to be HOME at the beach, because that was our favorite place of all. And we missed our dogs!!

But that's when everything started to go haywire.

Huffington Post, October 5, 2017

*An Epic Summer: It Started with a
Perfect European Trip... and Ended
with Hurricane Irma and Cancer.*

*In honor of #breastcancerawareness month - I'd like to
share my personal story with you because it's going to
take every single one of us to bring more awareness to
#cancer. Join me on my journey, won't you?*

IT BEGAN WITH EXHAUSTION.
MAYBE IT WAS NOTHING.
MAYBE A WHOLE LOT MORE.

I was more tired than I had ever been before. I was
sleeping 10 hours a night, and I was still exhausted.
Perhaps I should be rethinking my planned European
trip, but I just couldn't.

After all, my husband Mark and I had been planning
this trip for months. I was excited about the trip...my
first visit to Europe. My husband Mark works between
London and Paris every single week, so we planned for

me to meet him there in lieu of his flying back to the States.

The trip was perfect. It was wonderful to see Mark's life there, his work, his favorite places to eat. I really loved exploring both London and Paris. Even better, it was a sweet moment for both of us because it's been a roller coaster lifestyle this past year with his frequent trips working abroad.

But, I was also dog-tired. It really hit me that I simply couldn't keep up with him. What the...? He's 18 years older than I am, and I can't keep up with him? Okay, I admit, most people can't keep up with him, but I sure thought I'd done a pretty good job with it...until now.

That's when I first noticed a few changes. A change in my sleep and a change in my pace and my energy. I thought maybe I was just slowing down at the ripe old age of 33. But maybe it was my diet too. I've been in a battle with that for a long while. Maybe I'm not eating well enough.

Or maybe it's nothing? So, I shrugged it off...for a while.

Shortly after I got back to the States, I experienced some hardcore jet lag. I've traveled a lot in my short life, but this trip was hard to bounce back from. I kept thinking about how Mark does this every single week. He arrives home on Friday evenings and flies out on Monday mornings. So he never really changes or adapts to the 6 or 7 hours' time zone change...he just goes and goes. How does he do that?! I know I couldn't!

I remember around the same time I arrived home, I felt an uncomfortable sensation under my armpit. I felt around and noticed that I had a little bump there. Hmmm...I thought for a minute to recall if I'd done anything strenuous or hurt myself in any way. I didn't think so. But nonetheless, it was a little sore, so I thought maybe I pulled a muscle or I played too hard with my dogs. I didn't know what to think.

But the little bump quickly grew.

It started feeling like a golf ball in my armpit. I was more aware of it because I could feel the growing bump even more so now. I decided to feel around, explore further and do a breast self-exam.

Everything else felt fine...generally, I have pretty dense breast tissue anyway, so I thought it could be that I'm just lumpy. Nothing more.

I checked my appointment calendar and noticed that my next OB/GYN appointment was already on the books in about 30 days. No need to rush or worry unduly (or so I thought). I'll just wait to have my doctor do an exam and ask her about the lump.

As I mentioned, I'm only 33, and I don't go to a normal (primary care) doctor for anything. The only time I've ever visited a doctor was for my regular yearly well-woman exam. My life was pretty boring on the doctor front. I've never had surgery before, never broken a bone...nothing. I've been a pretty healthy woman and have been a pescatarian now for at least a year. I feel like I should be at the top of my game, right?

Running a successful business. *Check.*

Living a pescatarian lifestyle. *Check.*

Living with my better half and our two rescue pups, at the beach, in Florida. *Check. Check. Check.*

Life should be good. *Great, actually!* Then, why the hell am I so tired so often?

Maybe it's the wine I drink at dinner? Maybe I'm allergic to it?

I don't know.

All of this was running around in my head while waiting around for my doctor's appointment.

The day came to have my regular OB/GYN check-up. Everything checked out fine...until she did my breast exam. I explained to her that I have had this lump in my armpit.

As I was showing her where it was, I felt it again. Now it had grown to what felt like the size of a tennis ball. Ugh!

She asked me some questions. Did I get hit? Did I do anything out of the ordinary to hurt myself there? Do I have breast cancer in my family?

No.

And no.

To the third question, my answer was yes. My grandma passed away from breast cancer when she was around the age of 60.

The doctor's response wasn't alarming, "Let's send you over for an ultrasound just to make sure everything is good to go. But just know, this is super routine, nothing for you to worry about. This happens all the time."

I called and scheduled my ultrasound. The appointment was about two weeks later. I was still not really alarmed because I felt comforted by her words of, "...nothing for you to worry about."

The ultrasound turned into still another appointment two weeks after that one for a biopsy. Initially, they were going to just biopsy the lump area, but at the last minute the doctor came in while they were prepping me and said he'd reviewed the ultrasound once more and would like to take some additional biopsies of the area and of my lymph nodes in that area as well. As long as I was okay with that, he'd proceed with getting the order from my OB/GYN, and they'd proceed.

I was scared at this point because I didn't really understand what all this meant. The doctor who was doing the biopsies couldn't say anything until they were tested. Here I was *terrified* in a room with a bunch of doctors and nurses and no one had answers to anything. I felt vulnerable and helpless.

So, there I lay...in a lot of pain caused by all the times he removed tissue to biopsy with this gun-like-thing that kicked back every time he took a piece out of me. **Two. Three. Four. Five times, I counted. Six. Seven. I'm pretty sure I heard eight total times.**

After they did the biopsies, they shot a tiny marker in that area to "tag" (or mark) the areas where I was biopsied. To ensure those markers were in there correctly, they had to stand me up and walked me over to the mammogram machine to check the markers.

All I remember is standing in front of this machine I've never seen before, wondering what they were going to do—and the rest is history. I fainted. They caught me. I came to with them making me drink orange juice. The first thought that came to my head was weirdly, "Is this organic OJ?" and the second was, "Why was this happening?" I didn't understand.

I started crying and the nurse asked me what I needed. I said, "My mom!" Thankfully, my mom came with me that day and was in the waiting room. My mom came in, and it was like the clouds had parted and I was going to be okay. All it took was a comforting, motherly hug and kiss.

We finished up the outpatient patient paperwork and left.

I started thinking a lot about what had just happened. I'd never had a biopsy before, nor have I ever had a mammogram. So many things are happening and they are all firsts for me. It's scary as hell... and although I still don't know anything yet, I'm starting to worry that something is actually wrong with me.

Over the next week, thankfully, I started healing from the painful biopsies. I tried to get back into work and my regular schedule. I knew my doctor's office was to follow up in about a week. They said they would let us know if it's anything to worry about. But clearly, it's not since it's been a few days.

My cell phone rang on that Friday morning, and I could just tell by the tone of the doctor's voice that it wasn't good news.

She said something like, "Would you like to come into the office and talk about your results?" I was thinking, "Why can't you just tell me now? Why would I come to your office?!"

I said, "Nah, I'm just looking forward to hearing if you found anything."

BIG. DEEP. FREAKIN. PAUSE.

"Chelsea, it's all cancer."

"What do you mean ALL?" I asked.

She said, "All the biopsies came back as cancer."

I said, "All of them?"

She said, "Yes, ALL of them."

I broke down in tears and walked into the kitchen where my husband was. He chose not to travel that week since he missed both the ultrasound and the biopsies the week prior, and he wanted to be sure he was with me when I received the results. And boy, I was so glad he was there for me.

I handed him the phone as I began to cry hard.

All I heard Mark say to the doctor was, "I don't understand...what do you mean? What kind of cancer? How bad is it?"

I guess the doctor didn't know anything other than the results of the biopsy and that she had to send it along to an oncologist whom we would be meeting with to learn more about the results and next steps.

That was it. CANCER. Six horrifying letters.

So, there we were. Going into a weekend. With no answers. Only questions. Confusion. And those six letters.

"Maybe it's just something they have to remove, right? Maybe it's something as straight forward as a lumpectomy and then we're good!?" Mark said. He's so driven to fix the problem, find the solution... and I was stuck in WTF mode.

We made calls to our family. We all cried a lot.

Then, Monday came. We had an oncologist appointment at 4 p.m. **Unfortunately, Hurricane Irma had different plans. Although the weather was really bad, we went anyway. There was a big sign on the** door that said that the office was closed because of the hurricane.

ARE YOU KIDDING ME? We have to wait another day, another night... just because of a freaking hurricane that barely hit us (we live in the West Panhandle). **Okay, I get it...a hurricane IS a big deal. But when you find out you have cancer, and you're waiting for that one appointment to tell you everything you need to know, an even longer wait didn't sit so well with us.**

The next morning my husband called the office and he demanded we get seen that day. I remember him saying, "Please don't make us wait another day to understand what is happening. We found out my wife has cancer, and we don't know anything else beyond that. So please help us. PLEASE!" I could hear it in his voice that he was scared too.

They were able to squeeze me in at the end of the day, around 4 p.m. We arrived and sat in the waiting room for what felt like hours. I looked around and the office was full of elderly people with chemo ports and bald heads.

Was this really happening to me at my young age?

We were finally called back into the office, and Mark and I walked into the room and sat down. They weighed me, checked my vitals...the normal stuff. Again, we waited.

The doctor came in with this very calm voice and said, "Let's start with you telling me what you know so far." I thought, "We don't know a damn thing other than they found cancer inside my body and no one seems to know anything else."

Mark had to do most of the talking for me. We (mostly he) explained what we knew.

She asked how I was feeling. We explained.

Finally, after sitting in what felt like hours of silence she said, "You have triple negative breast cancer. It's a very aggressive form of cancer, and it was found in the lump and the lymph nodes in your armpit."

At this point I'm only hearing about 10% of what is being said. Thank God for Mark, because he's a very inquisitive guy. He asked a million questions. Things we didn't understand were being talked about. Drugs, treatment, next steps. I could see his head just spinning, because all he wanted to do was take the information and come up with a simple formula to fix it.

But he couldn't.

We just had to learn the things we didn't know.

She said she couldn't give us more information just yet because I haven't had the scheduled PET/CT scan. She said that she's going in blind, so she needs to get that data first before we can really understand the plan in much greater detail.

She ordered a **PET/CT** scan **STAT** but also put the order in for a surgeon to install a port and do an **EKG STAT** as well, which scared me because she was clearly wanting us to move fast on this. Later I realized it was because the cancer I have is so aggressive that days really **DID** matter.

I went for my PET/CT scan within a day. Then, we went back to the doctor...yet again. **Now came the news that shocked me to the bone.** Low and behold, the aggressive cancer had not only spread from my armpit/breast to lymph nodes in my clavicle, but potentially to lymph nodes in my neck. The diagnosis was definitely Stage 3C and likely early Stage 4. In either case, given my age and health history, the treatment was the same.

However, we had some good news...When my doctor came in and gave us the news of the PET/CT scan, the first thing she said was, "I have good news and I'm going to celebrate with a drink tonight!" I could tell she was relieved but didn't understand why. What I didn't know at the time was my husband asked for a private meeting with the doctor after our first appointment, before the CT scan, to inquire on what she really thought about my diagnosis. Mark told me the doctor told him she was extremely concerned on the severity of my cancer.

The good news was that there was consensus that my treatment will be focused on surgery/cure, even though the fact that activity was spotted in the PET/CT scan in my neck was still concerning.

At the urging of almost everyone we spoke to, we decided to get a second opinion. Our neighbor put us in touch with a doctor at UVA (The University of Virginia) that reviewed our films and told us that while they would love for me to participate in a clinical trial, the cancer is quite severe, and that I need to start chemo *immediately.* I guess good news is relative...

From there, a whirlwind of appointments, next steps, plans and paperwork happened. From there, my life changed. Forever.

Chapter 2

AN AUTUMN OF STRUGGLE

You don't think about breast cancer when you're 33.

As you may have guessed, Mark and I never got to Greece. I had no idea that trip to London and Paris would be our last. And it makes me so happy we took it when we did. It was truly EPIC. I'm so dang grateful we went. It was by far the best time we've had together, and we've had a lot of amazing times.

As for the lump, I noticed it in late June and didn't see the doctor for the ultrasound that ultimately revealed my cancer until the beginning of August. And that's really my only regret about this whole awful process—that I didn't go in sooner. It's possible my cancer wouldn't have been Stage 4 at that point; maybe it would have been smaller and more manageable. But maybe not.

It was a difference of only a few weeks.

Anyway, at the time, cancer was something that didn't seem possible. I had always been perfectly healthy. I thought the lump might be something, especially since it was growing so fast, so I told a few close friends, my mom and Mark. I made the doctor's appointment, and of course I kept it. But I'm generally "lumpy" and thought it was no big deal. There was no sense of OH MY GOD I NEED TO DO THIS TOMORROW!

Like I said, you don't think about breast cancer when you're 33.

But it can still happen.

Huffington Post, October 23, 2017
The New Normal: Everything is Different. Nothing is the Same. But, I Sure Do Miss "Me."

THIS IS REALLY HAPPENING. I HAVE BREAST CANCER.

It was all a blur at this point, like watching a movie on fast-forward. I vaguely remember the conversations, but there were, what felt like, hundreds. We don't just work with one doctor—we work with *four*. Our cancer team consists of an oncologist, surgeon, radiologist and reconstructive plastic surgeon. Not to mention the dozens of nurses that are there every step of the way.

It truly takes a village to care for a cancer patient. I had no idea the complexity of what had just entered my life!

As you can imagine, my husband is the one taking all the notes at this point. I've been told most cancer patients only hear about 10% of what's being said due to the whirlwind of having cancer, communicating with all the doctors/nurses, managing a long list of medications and keeping up with all the appointments. And, with a different doctor's appointment almost every single day, everything seems to be going at warp speed. Lastly, given the aggressiveness of my triple negative breast cancer, we get new instructions/plans/requests daily that have to be handled STAT! It is *totally overwhelming!*

Literally within days of our finding out about my cancer, I had to wrap my head around the fact that they planned to nuke my entire body with poison for four months, so we can save my life. And we needed to do it, STAT!

Clearly, this isn't something we can just spend some time to reflect on and weigh options. **With early Stage 4 cancer, and a second opinion telling me to not even consider clinical trials and start chemo ASAP, there is almost no time to even think about what is going on.** You just jump in and pray for the best.

That's when I knew this wasn't just an illness we get medication for and fix. That's when it all sunk in for me. This is really happening. I have cancer. **And the cancer is angry as hell.**

YOU'RE GOING TO PUT THAT THING WHERE?

The first step in receiving chemo treatments is to install a port...*in my chest!* Apparently, chemo cannot be administered via a peripheral IV. It was my greatest fear at this point. The idea of having to put me under and install this foreign object in my chest, connecting it to a vein that goes directly to my heart. *It sounded like something from The Matrix!*

I've never had an operation, been under anesthesia, broken a bone, or even had a stitch. I was terrified! For a moment, I even forgot all the worries about having cancer. I couldn't get my head around what is being installed in my body. This may seem like a small operation for most people but, for someone who has never had an operation, **this is now my biggest fear.**

Because time was everything, I had the port installed a few days later, AND they also started chemo that same day. So, not only was I under anesthesia in the morning of the port install, we left surgery and went straight to the clinic for my first six-hour chemo session. Mark asked several times if this was something we should be doing the day we start chemo. Everyone said, "No worries." Looking back, I would not recommend this to anyone...

It was the scariest day of my life. Hands down! I woke up from the operation in the recovery room very disoriented and remember Mark telling me we have to get going to start chemo. One fear behind me, but now another one in front of me. **I now have a device protruding from my chest to remind me every second of each day that I have cancer.** Mark is now helping me to the car so I can go get chemo. What could possibly happen next?

I asked Mark, "Was that the worst... or is the worst still coming?"

He said, "I have no idea."

And we sat in silence as we drove to the other clinic to start my chemo.

CHELSEA, RED DEVIL...RED DEVIL, CHELSEA...

Let's just say, I didn't pass the first chemo session with flying colors. Because of the severity of the cancer and the combination of the chemo drugs being administered, I had every side effect you could possibly imagine (some exacerbated by the port operation earlier, too).

If you haven't heard of the "red devil," then you've been blessed with a good life. That's exactly what they call one of my chemo drugs. Yes, the drug is red, but there is a reason it is not nicknamed "red angel." This drug is one of the most aggressive chemo drugs and has some pretty harsh side effects. I guess my partner in crime these days is poison, **because it's the only thing that will save my life.** (Ironic, huh?) Once I got over the fact that poison is being pumped through my body, I now think in my head, "It's on, red devil. Let's do this!"

Now that I'm knee deep in chemo, all the horror stories I heard came true: weakness, headaches, dizziness, nausea, body aches, skin sensitivity (and that was just about all bodily functions that were impacted). In addition, a lot of simple things got a whole lot harder, like, brushing my teeth, taking a shower, eating, walking my dogs, etc. Thankfully, chemo sessions are every two weeks, so I had some time to prepare for my next session. After my first session, it took me 5 days just to be able to slowly get around the house. Day 6 was the first day I left the house. I was alright overall, but my body ached and my headaches were **pain I had never experienced before.**

WHAT? I MIGHT HAVE BRAIN CANCER?

My doctor stressed to us that if anything (ANYTHING at all) is different or has changed, to let her know. **That's why we let her know my headaches were still massive**, so we went in for a checkup on my off week. Blood work was alright, a little dehydrated, but she said, "I'm concerned about your headaches. We need to get your brain scanned to ensure the cancer hasn't spread. Let's schedule you for an MRI, STAT!"

If that didn't scare someone, then I don't know what would. **We knew the cancer had metastasized. But did it go further? Was it now in my brain?**

First, the hospital called and informed us the first open slot on the schedule is two weeks from that day. Within 15 minutes of informing our oncologist of the delay, magically, we had an appointment for the brain MRI the next day. With everything that was going on, the fact that there is so much urgency (STAT!) around my entire treatment regimen is scary in and of itself. And now, in addition to breast cancer, I may have brain cancer. All night long I'm thinking, WTF?

Luckily, the morning after the MRI, we were told that I was clear of brain cancer. So, now we knew the cancer had not metastasized anymore and had stayed localized in my armpit, breast, clavicle and neck.

What a relief. Good news all around. We were so grateful. **I may have cried myself to sleep that night.** The good cry.

PRIORITIES CHANGE: HOW I SPEND MY TIME AND MONEY CHANGE. LIFE JUST CHANGES.

Now, here I sit...with my hair slowing falling out each day. **I'm surfing Amazon for cancer books instead of cookbooks. Trying to find the best place to buy hats and scarves to cover my head instead of new house décor or a cool new vintage t-shirt.** Everything I'm doing seems to focus on having cancer (kind of like having blinders on and that's all I can see). Everything is different. Nothing is the same. But, I sure do miss "me."

I'm just glad that the port surgery was out of the way, the first chemo was out of the way, and I was feeling more human. But yet, all I have to look forward to is to do this all over again every 2 weeks. How do you even wrap your head around that? **Especially, when you have no choice.**

We headed back to the surgeon's office to get my stitches out and for her to check to ensure the port is all good. All went well...but by this time, the surgeon also had our PET/CT scan info and let us know that **the cancer found above my clavicle is inoperable, so we need to be hopeful that the chemo + radiation in my future can take care of it.** But she says, "For now, let's not focus there. We will keep an eye on it." I believed her, I have so much trust in this lady.

We finished the appointment and headed back home. Mark says "What do you want to do to celebrate?"

I looked at him with confusion and replied, "Celebrate what?"

"You got your stitches out from your port operation!" he exclaimed.

It was probably the first time I laughed in days. I said, "Actually...I want pizza!"

I was as surprised as he was when he heard the word "Pizza"...because I haven't had much of an appetite (one of the many downsides to chemo). But, I was craving pizza.

So, we had pizza to celebrate this small milestone.

Mark and I started discussing the doctors' aggressive plan, that included four months of chemo, then a double mastectomy along with the removal of lymph nodes below my clavicle and my armpit, followed by daily radiation treatment for 6.5 weeks and then, finally, reconstructive surgery. **It was going to be a long journey.**

For now, I'm just taking it day by day...and I look forward to a break from the cold hospitals and clinics, the feeling of stepping into a whole other world and having to leave what you know behind. I want all that to go away, so I can just get some peace.

I knew I'd have the support from my family and friends. However, I didn't know what help would feel like. You see, I'm a giver. It's my love language. Nevertheless, to have people give to me meant that all I wanted to do was give back. If I couldn't give back to them, I didn't feel whole, and I didn't feel myself. I felt bad when they were giving me so much love and support. The problem with wanting to give back was that I was exhausted.

All of the texts. All the phone calls. It simply became too much for me. Thankfully, Mark was there to help me sort through all the well wishes. He now takes most of the messages and receives the gifts for me. I'm overwhelmed in all the best ways, but I just had no idea how much people cared and wanted to help.

It's just a sweet reminder reminding me that there is so much good in the world... even when it feels hard. The goodness of our community has been breathtaking.

And, thankfully there are sunsets...and sunsets keep on giving. My sweet friends and I drove on to the beach (because I didn't have enough strength to get out there on my own), and we watched the most epic sunset. It was a perfect night...and I think we all were just happy to be there, in awe of our surroundings, enjoying the perfect sunset. What more did I need?

ROUND 2 AND 3: DING, DING, DING!

For a split second on the beach, I almost forgot I had cancer. Now I'm home and preparing for the next rounds of chemo. Mentally preparing to do this all over again is not something for the faint of heart. Knowing what to expect and reading what people say about the further you get into chemo, the harder it may become. But the nurses reassured me that everyone is different. I might take it like a champ this time, and I might not.

As the process goes, they do my blood work and clear me for chemo. Then, they take me back to my chair, husband in tow, and another 6-hours in the cancer center. The entire day is spent at the clinic once again. My reactions to the second and third round of chemo were very similar. I felt like I had the flu for about six days, Days 3 and 4 after chemo are the worst for body aches...the most pain I've ever felt. It felt as if **my body was covered in bruises** and it hurt to even glide my hand over it. From my face to my thighs, this is how it felt. I could barely move. **I literally went into the bathroom and undressed so I could look in the mirror and see if I actually had bruises on my body.** I didn't, but it sure felt like it. Eventually, Day 6 rolled around, and I felt somewhat human again. **Thank God for Day 6. It's what I looked forward to.**

THE CANCER WILL NOT DECIDE...I WILL.

This, my friends, is what my life is like now. Appointments, blood checks, chemo, sickness, and repeat. I work in my business on my best days and my crappiest days, because it continues to remind me that I'm human. I haven't lost myself just yet. **But how do I plan for the future while I'm stuck in "Groundhog Day?"** Do I cancel my upcoming vacation or do I go? Do I chance getting sick and having a setback for this whole process? Or do I stay cooped up in my house until it's over?

(Spoiler alert: I cancelled.)

Funny how your priorities can shift just like that. Beyond that, I'm ready to take control because, **if you let it, cancer will take everything from you.** I have decided, no matter how hard, I will own this. I will not let cancer decide everything for me. I will stay empowered! One of the ways I am doing this is by sharing my story. **No matter how bad I feel, I want to take the time and give**

back by raising awareness, so less people have to go through this dreaded process alone.

When my hair started falling out, it was pretty dramatic. I knew it would be, but I never thought I was that attached to it, so I thought I could deal.

(Funny story—there was a time when I was a bit more attached to my hair. Back when I was 19, I briefly joined the Navy. It's kind of a long story that's in my first book if you want more details, but the most traumatic moment was when they took my long, blonde ponytail and *chopped it off*, just like that, with no warning at all! I was beyond upset, I was mortified.

But I got over the hair thing when I got older. In fact, I cut my hair short twice in order to donate it to Locks of Love…a charity that makes wigs for cancer patients.

Yeah. Irony.)

I did more than just deal. **I handed the buzz cutter to my husband and said, "Shave it. Shave it all off."** I'm going to decide when my hair falls out. The cancer WILL NOT decide for me. I'm owning this. And that was that. It was done and over with. I took my hair off; cancer had nothing to do with it! Mark has decided to show his support by not shaving until I am cured. I said, "Not shaving? How is that showing support?" His response,

"**I'm going to grow enough hair for the both of us.**" I smiled and knew with his presence/support/love, I would be OK.

But, there was one thing that was still puzzling me. After my husband buzzed my head, I got this eerie feeling about his attitude. In my mind, while we don't really talk about it, I know what the worst outcome of this disease is. As long as I've known Mark, he is always preparing for the worst possible outcome. No matter what he does, he is always planning, checking, double checking, etc., so, if the worst possible outcome happens, he is always prepared. However, he seems to have changed. When it comes to my cancer, he seems to only focus on what would be the best outcomes for me. From chemo preparation, to the surgeries...everything. I finally asked him about this, because it didn't sit right with me. He is so predictable and now everything I actually thought I understood about him was changing.

So, I asked him. "Why aren't you preparing for the worst? As long as I've known you, you've always been the one preparing for the worst, and I don't feel like you're really thinking about the severity of this cancer... and planning for the worst thing that could happen should probably be on our radar!"

At first, he responded and somewhat dismissed my question. Then, he came back to me a few days later.

Apparently, my question concerned him as he needed some time to reflect why he was being different. Then he explained it to me. He said, "I don't agree with your perception of how I am acting. What do you mean not preparing for the worst? In my mind, this IS the worst."

I smiled as now it all made sense again.

Well, now we know what the worst is. And it turns out, Mark was still probably right. The actual worst, those words you don't want to hear, that thing you don't want to face isn't something you can really prepare for.

When I wrote that post, I said I wasn't going to let cancer take everything away from me, and damn, I tried my hardest to make sure it didn't. But in the end, that turned out to be something I couldn't control, even by doing everything I was supposed to do, even when chemo was so hard I said I couldn't take it anymore and Mark was the only thing that kept me going by basically forcing me to stick with it.

Facebook, November 4, 2017

It's hard. It's really, really hard right now.

So many of my favorite things have been stripped from my life. Little things like wine and a nice dinner with my husband, the smell and taste of coffee in the morning and a simple walk with my dogs. All of that is really hard right now. Right now, I'm lucky if I can keep green juice and Cheerios in my stomach.

But, for the first time in my entire life - I appreciate so many sweet moments that I didn't have time for before. I talk about how beautiful the sunset is each night, the mornings when my husband and I eat Cheerios together, and the ability to still taste pumpkin pie when a friend brings it over.

Pain does change you. Today, I'm thankful for the pain - because I know there is profound change happening... and I look forward to meeting "me" on the other side of this.

CHAPTER 3

SWEET INSPIRATION

November, 2017

I was in the middle of chemo, so even though Thanksgiving was coming, I wasn't exactly thinking about turkey and cranberry sauce. Instead, I was looking around the chemo room and seeing that so many people were alone in there. It kind of hurt my heart.

I knew, even though I was miserable as hell, I had so much to be thankful for. I had Mark and was surrounded by so much love and support from friends and family. A lot of the time, they'd pack me a bag of goodies to take to chemo that brightened my day, stuff to help keep me comfortable and pass the time during the six hours I spent getting poison pumped into my body. Just basic stuff like really nice hand lotion and lip balm for when my skin felt dry and adult coloring books and crayons for when I got bored and herbal tea to sip and hard candy to suck on to help fight the nausea.

So, I'd come in with my bag full of all this cool stuff, stuff that really helped. And I'd look around the room and see so many people suffering alone, with nothing. So I ended up giving most of my stuff away.

Which gave me an idea...

What if I curated a bunch of the same goodies that I was using during the chemo process, and put it all in a bag and gave it away to people who needed it? I pulled together all the stuff I was using and realized it made a pretty rad bag. What if there was a way to get these bags to breast cancer patients who needed them all over the country, for free? Or even the world (when I dream, I dream big!)?

That's when the Foye Belle Foundation and the Blue Bag movement was born.

I named the foundation after my grandmother—she's the one I mentioned back when my OB-GYN asked me if there had been any breast cancer in my family. I remember being a little girl and learning about my grandmother's breast cancer diagnosis. It was bad and in her bones, and while I didn't know much, I could tell from the way people were talking and acting that that didn't mean anything good.

Through it all, she had so much love and light left in her, and it left a lasting impression on my life and the lives of many others. She died when I was 11 or 12, and it was really sad. She was lovely and classy and I adored her. But I figured dying from cancer was just a sad thing that happened to old people.

Now I knew that wasn't the case.

From the moment I was diagnosed with breast cancer, I thought about my grandma and the suffering and pain she endured. Did she have the support she needed? When I realized that I could actually do something to help provide support to other people who were suffering, naming the foundation after her was a no-brainer.

As for the blue bags…there was a reason behind that too.

The face of breast cancer is often presented in the media by models with beautiful bodies and fake scars. Well, I know what breast cancer really looks like. It's CTs, surgeries, amputations, biopsies, MRIs, X-rays, radiation, chemo, IVs, blood tests, medications, check-ups, fear, worry, hate, anger, confusion, sadness, loneliness, anxiety, depression, insomnia and pain. Breast cancer is not pretty. And it's no pink ribbon.

No offense to the pink ribbons people wear for breast cancer and all the money that's been raised because of them. But if breast cancer is a color, I'm pretty sure it's blue. Because it makes you feel blue to the very core.

Hence, the Blue Bag movement.

Facebook, November 22, 2017

Hey y'all -

I've been working behind the scenes on something near and dear to my heart... and now it's ready for the world.

We created The Foye Belle Foundation to support those going through this awful disease and especially for those that are doing it alone.

I was fortunate enough to be surrounded by a great deal of support -- and I've received some of the most amazing goodies to help me through the bad days... but, unfortunately - that's not the case for so many people I've met.

Most people I meet at the cancer center come alone (and with no goodies in tow)... so, early on, I started giving away so much of my stuff because they needed it worse than I did. Thus, the foundation was born and the blue bag movement is finally becoming a reality.

I can't do it alone - your support and donations are so appreciated. The blue bag movement will help so many people and I'm crazy thrilled to be spearheading the process.

Here's the website for more info: https://foyebelle.org

Big love and Happy Thanksgiving! I hope you're thankful for a lot this year... but, be extra thankful for your health...

Chelsea

CHAPTER 4

SOLAMAR

Y ou might be wondering how a person who spent the majority of her time either in chemo or recovering from chemo managed to design and launch a website (along with a super cool t-shirt to sell on that website to raise money for the foundation). I kind of have a secret…that's what I do for a living. The business I founded and am still attempting to run, Solamar Agency, handles projects for businesses that include things like design, branding and website development. Full disclosure: they'll be helping me publish this book too, even when I'm not around to direct them. I've got an amazing team and they rock, and I know they'll keep Solamar strong in my absence.

When I was growing up, I never, ever expected to launch a half-million-dollar business. I was one of those people who didn't fit in one of those convenient boxes they try to put you in in high school—you know, future teacher, future doctor, future auto mechanic—so everyone is in on the game, everyone knows what they're preparing you for and everyone and everything pushes you in that direction.

I tried, but I just couldn't find a direction to be pushed *in*. I was drifting.

I took some college classes, but I had no idea what to study. I made a disastrous attempt to join the military (remember the haircut incident?), and I was so miserable my mom had to rescue me by convincing my C.O. to let me out. I married and divorced twice before I was 24, just kind of bouncing around looking for home, not knowing quite where I belonged in the world.

But the thing is, this whole time, I had a secret weapon even I didn't know was there.

I was willing to *work*.

At 19, I talked my way into a job at a global distribution company that was based in my area. Okay, full disclosure, I more like *stalked* my way into the job. I drove the owner of the company crazy, calling him every day and even showing up at his office until he finally broke down and gave me a job answering phones as a Customer Service rep.

That job saved my life.

I discovered that the world of work was the place I'd been looking for—the place where I was good at things, where I actually belonged. I had this knack for figuring out what people needed and then figuring out how to give it to them. Just by observing where the company was struggling or overwhelmed and working my butt off to solve the problem, I taught myself to be a bookkeeper, a sales rep, a supervisor, even a techie. Within three years, I had worked my way all the way up the ladder to become Director of Sales and Business Development, reporting directly to the VP.

I was 23.

That's when I decided to start a company.

My current company sent me to a trade show in San Diego, California. I'd never been to one before, or even ordered room service at a hotel! I'd traveled a little for the job, but this trip was different because they put me up in the first really nice hotel I'd ever stayed in in my life. The room, the décor, the room service, it all blew me away to the point where my brain was just on fire. And instead of falling asleep in my beautiful bed in my beautiful room, I sat up all night thinking, "How can I do this *all the time*?" I knew I had climbed about as far as I could at the company where I was working. If I was going to have a life where I'd get to travel around and meet new people all the time, as opposed to once in a while, I had to start my own business.

So that night, sitting on my comfy hotel bed with the brown and white polka dot comforter, I brainstormed a way to make it happen. I had learned so much at my job I felt like I could really do any kind of work anyone might ask me to do. But one of the main things I had learned is that when you get right down to it, everything is marketing. So, I decided I was starting a marketing company. And I named it Solamar Marketing, after the Hotel Solamar, which was my inspiration.

Since that fateful trip, the now officially named Solamar Agency has grown...a lot. We're a half-million-dollar boutique marketing agency focusing on branding and design, with a team of 14 very different people, each with their own superhero skill, who come together to support businesses, nonprofits and business people through eye-catching design, rock star branding and persuasive marketing messages.

Hey, what did you expect from a marketer?

As I'm writing this, I'm working on transitioning Solamar to those very 14 capable hands (I guess I mean 28 capable hands!), who will continue to serve our clients the way we always have. It's hard. Really hard, letting go of this thing I poured so much of my heart into for so many years. But I didn't build it alone, and that's how I know Solamar will be fine without me. Thanks, in part, to Sam.

Sam George has been with Solamar for about seven years and is now our main designer and just everything to us. He originally was an actor and even studied acting at Carnegie-Mellon. He taught himself design as a side gig... and the rest is history. He's brilliant in so many ways!

He is truly the best soul. He's not only become such an integral part of our work here at Solamar, he's my friend and my family too. His whole family is my family. I love him dearly... and he'll be the one taking over and running Solamar and bringing it home every damn day. I'm truly grateful for his love, dedication and hard work. And that he *really* wants to take over Solamar! I wouldn't want it going to anyone else.

So Solamar will continue to support my husband and the Foye Belle Foundation, which is good because since that first announcement just before Thanksgiving, we've lined up some wholesale partners to provide some of the goodies, and as of today, we have raised over $50K. We've shipped out hundreds of blue bags and are ready to do so much more. It's been so amazing.

After I'm gone, Mark is going to continue on with the foundation and work to raise more awareness, reach more people and get more Blue Bags out to the people that need them the most.

If there as been an upside to my "cancer journey," this is it. I love it. It's my favorite thing ever, and I'm so happy I'll be leaving this legacy behind. (And by the way, all proceeds from this book are going directly to the Foye Belle Foundation, too. So, thank you so much for buying it, means more to me than you know!)

CHAPTER 5

A WINTER OF HOPE

Huffington Post, December 20, 2017
All I Want for Christmas is Chemo...and to be Cured.

It's been 98 days since I found out I have cancer.

98 days. 2,352 hours. 141,120 minutes to be exact.

It feels like a lifetime.

Actually, it feels like a whole different life.

I'm tired of feeling sick and sore...of feeling like my life just stopped and my cancer has started to define everything I do, everything I am. I truly try to make it all different. I push at it with everything I have. But, I'm just not strong enough. I'm too tired, too weak. I just want it all to go away.

As I sit here writing this, I keep rubbing my face because I'm extremely tired and sore from no sleep over the last few weeks. (I've been up because of the dreaded body aches and the wired brain from all the steroids. It's how I spend my nights these days.) I pull my hand away from my face, and I suddenly realize I rubbed most of my remaining eyebrows off. I was hoping they'd stay put, because my eyebrows are the only hair I have left. But, this is life now. It's official. My eyebrows are almost gone, too.

Needless to say, my figure is not mine anymore either. I look sick. I don't even look like Mr. Clean anymore...more like an alien. Especially when my friends capture the moments we're together...I don't even recognize myself in the pictures. I'm all covered up, because I'm freezing, I'm flushed because my body is so damn angry at me, I'm thin because I'm selective these days on what I'm putting into my body, and I move like I'm 100 years old.

In 98 short days my lifestyle has changed, my body has changed...everything has changed. Daily, I dance around the fact that I have cancer....trying to find ways through it or around it or just to simply forget about it. However, it's there reminding me that no one is safe from cancer, not even me. What I thought to be my healthy 33-year-old body, was not so invincible. So, I'll continue to wake up every day with my new priorities in mind and focus on my cure no matter what it takes...all while being grateful that I am alive.

Even with no eyebrows.

It's the little things that matter these days. Being thankful is one of those things. The last 3 months of my life have been an absolute roller coaster. Just when I feel like I'm starting to make progress, everything changes. I feel like we've taken three steps forward and five steps back. But there's a growing sense of perspective in the madness of it all. A series of life-lessons, introspection and self-growth.

OH, THE PEOPLE YOU'LL MEET.

My new life brings experiences that include new friends I am meeting, and together we are sharing a journey. These people are fighting back with me during chemo sessions, scans/tests, and doctors' appointments. All the while, everyone—the patients, the nurses, the doctors—we're all just trying to survive.

During one of my chemo sessions, I sat next to a lady who was diagnosed with Stage 4, incurable cancer and had been doing chemo for over 2 years just to "buy" some more time. She mentioned, in a "matter of fact" tone, that she only had about six months to live and the chemo is just allowing her to spend a little extra time with her family. She told us that she's in the process of building a house, so her husband and her son could start anew once she's gone. Ugh...I can't even imagine her desperation and anxiety.

She was literally picking out faucets for her family's new house the day I met her! I couldn't believe it. Chatting with her, unless she mentioned it, you would never know her condition. While we were talking, she was accessorizing a home she'll never live in. I was speechless—ready to just pour tears. I'm sure she's grieving, but she seemed to be in good spirits and understood the reality of wanting to finish a few more things before giving in to the disease. She was absolutely lovely and comforting. Yet, as I sat there I thought, "How did we get here? Is this really happening?" I was literally holding in the tears. But what I really wanted to do is let the tears flow freely while hearing her story.

Another lady I met during this process really made a profound impact on my journey so far. She was the first person I met at my very first chemo session. We shared a room together. She explained what the medical staff was doing to me, what to expect, and what to do when I got home. She talked about her trials, her frustrations, and her hope. She was very inspiring due to her incredible sass, feistiness, and genuine curiosity when it came to the process. She seemed so in control when the nurses or doctors would talk with her. She wanted to know everything, so she questioned everything. Because it was her body, she bravely took control of each part of it. I admired her for that! And, above all - she will be my friend for life. Not just because she showed me how to use my chemo chair (it's heated and I had no idea!), but because she's a very talented artist and she painted a picture of my sweet dogs! My heart melted! She's now finished with her chemo...and I couldn't be more proud of her. But, secretly, I'm super bummed because I miss her dearly.

One gal I can't get out of my head is the one that walked into the waiting room with sunshine just beaming from every part of her body. She was fighting hard just like all of us, has massive cancer, and she comes in all pepped up and ready to kick ass. She is one of the happiest people I have experienced...and she made me smile, laugh, and forget (even if for a minute) that we're sitting there waiting to get poison pumped into our bodies. She was a breath of fresh air, and I always look for her every time I get there (and secretly hope she's coming if I don't see her). She's practically bursting with happiness, and her grace is the absolute best. Even though she doesn't know it, she helps me get through every chemo session just by being herself.

In addition to the people I've met along the way, there's also been this amazing outreach from people I've never met. People that have battled (or are battling) cancer in different states across the country and even in different countries across the world. They have been reaching out to me, sharing their stories...all because I started sharing mine. Alas, the reason I chose to share was with hopes that I'd reach more people with my story and (hopefully!) be a glimmer of light for someone else battling their own battle. Funny thing though...they have been my glimmer of light that have pushed me through the worst nights. Their stories are empowering and have made me feel less alone, less isolated.

I had someone reach out and say, "I know you don't know me, but I live in the area and I was diagnosed at 36, and it's all so scary. But if you ever need anything, lunch brought to you, coffee...let me know!"

Later that week I heard from this stranger-friend again...and she said, "I'm running in the 30A half marathon on Sunday and was wondering if you would mind if I gave you a shout out during my run and on social media? When I run I think, if I can make it through chemo, I can make it through this next mile! It's a big world but with you being so close, I think my energy can help you the most. Is this okay with you?"

Of course I said yes! I was blown away by the support. And to top it off...I finally got to meet this stranger-friend at my next chemo session. She was there doing follow up testing. I hugged her tightly and realized that she, too, will be a friend forever.

I've had dozens of people reach out and say things like "I found this lump and I don't have health insurance, so I've not gone in to get it checked out."

That breaks my heart into a million pieces.

WE ARE STARTING TO UNDERSTAND THE PROCESS... KIND OF.

At the beginning of all of this, we thought the chemo process was going to be every other week for four months.

Boy, have things changed.

After our fourth chemo session (and the end of Phase One!), the doctor told us that she'd like to try an experimental drug during this next phase. So, Phase Two will be a combination of two drugs: one weekly (normal protocol) and one every three weeks (experimental drug). And to top it off, we have to extend the process an extra month. Meaning goodbye to only having chemo for four months. It will now be at least five months.

I was shocked. Pissed. Bummed. All of that...and so much more!

I was truly feeling like I could see the light at the end of the tunnel, and now everything went pitch black again. Weekly chemo and an extra month to boot—it crushed me! I literally was thinking, "I don't know if I can do this anymore!"

But, onward I went. Mostly because my husband said I had to. Mark has been my rock and, just when I think I can't do it anymore, he pushes me and shows me

1-800-TO-WELLS (1-800-869-3557)

Thank you for using our ATM.
We appreciate your business.

Member FDIC

NSM-210WW-0715

We'd love to hear about your experiences
with our ATMs.
Twitter: @WellsFargo
Facebook: Facebook.com/WellsFargo

WELLS FARGO

Date:	08/30/18
Time:	10:00 AM
Location:	SANDY/SPRINGS
ATM:	0479K

Customer Card: XXXXXXX9389
Transaction #:   8225
Transaction: Deposit To checking
Amount: $1,290.00
To: Nancy x-6387
Deposit credit Date: 08/30/18

Available Balance: $2,416.97

DEPOSIT AVAILABILITY:
The full amount of your deposit is
included in your available balance now.

DETAILS OF BILLS DEPOSITED:

```
17 x $20 = $340.00
 7 x $50 = $350.00
 6 x $100 = $600.00
```

Thank you for banking with Wells Fargo.
For questions, call 1-800-869-3557
Business customers
call 1-800-225-5935.

that I actually can. He never gives me a break and I love him for it. I would not be where I am today without him.

So I did what only I could do...I started to mentally prepare myself for this next phase. I was ready.

Here we go, Phase Two! Let's do this.

And then I hear the words, "I'm so sorry, we aren't going to be able to give you chemo today. Your blood work is not good—your body isn't strong enough to accept the treatment."

"What does that mean?" I said.

"It means you go home, and we try again next week."

And it also means my chemo schedule just got extended another week.

I just can't face this "setback."

What's next, universe!?

Oh, right. Thanksgiving. You know the holiday I won't be able to be with my family, because I'll be dog sick, in bed, trying to survive due to the chemo the day before.

Thankfully, I was able to get chemo on Thanksgiving week, but unfortunately the next two chemo sessions I was turned away again, because my body wasn't healthy enough to accept treatment. Now we're three weeks behind.

Setback after setback...will this ever end?

I GUESS I NEED TO GET USED TO CHANGE...CHANGE IS THE NEW NORMAL.

Now, knowing I'm not taking chemo like a champ, we discussed the delays with my doctor. She's concerned my body is not healthy enough to withstand the combination of the normal protocol chemo treatment, along with the experimental drug, so we need to make some changes. As a result, we're going to remove the experimental drug from my treatment plan completely and see if that allows my blood counts/liver counts to rebound. It's a bad thing to continually be turned away each week as, without getting chemo, the cancer can grow and become even more angry. That's why we have to do everything we can to stay on track. Consistency is important at this point (along with a little adaptability and flexibility).

Our doctor is concerned about my blood counts and liver counts as the standard protocol does not have this effect on most patients. As a result, she suggested another CT scan to ensure the cancer has not spread to other organs within my body.

Yeah. Not the most exciting news. Anything that starts with, "Let's do a scan to ensure there are no other masses on your organs" is never a fun thing to hear, because then my mind wanders into the unknown. What the hell—how is this happening? Is cancer going to kill me? Will I truly get out of this alive? Is this the end?

You know what I'm talking about...those kinds of awful, fatalistic, terrified thoughts.

But, what I know to be true is that my doctor is very cautious. She doesn't gamble or guess. She wants to rule things out. Even if the CT scan is going overboard, it's the only way for her to know for sure what's happening inside my body. She does think it's the chemo that's not playing well with my body, not necessarily a mass somewhere else. But we won't know until we can rule it out.

We sat in the waiting room, waiting to be called back for yet another scan. A nurse came out and said, "Chelsea Berler."

I stood up thinking I'd be going in, but instead she handed me a white drink and said, "Drink this and we'll be back to get you in 30 minutes."

Okayyyyy. (I totally thought she was handing me her Starbucks :))

I've never been asked to drink anything prior to a scan before so I guess this is definitely different. They are doing a specific abdominal scan, focusing mostly on my liver.

So, I drank it.

It was awful. Like, for real. It looked like eggnog, but it was NOT eggnog! Secretly, I pretended it was a really delicious drink (Mark was laughing at the faces I was making. He almost made me spit it out). You know, the kind of alcoholic drink you'd love to have when fears are high. The kind that helps you sit back, relax and say, "I got this—piece of cake!"

But, it's also been 98 days since I had a drop of alcohol too.

30 minutes went by, and I was escorted back to the CT room. The usual instructions happen. They explain that they are going to inject some type of substance into my port so they can scan and see any activity.

I felt a new strength pop up in me...I blurted out, "No, I don't want you to access my port today. It's sore and I'm tired of being poked there!"

I could feel my bottom lip quivering...trying to hold back the tears.

The CT person looked at me with confusion and said, "Normally all cancer patients want to have this done through their port because their veins in their arms are shot at this point. Are you sure? Because I may struggle a bit to find a vein in your arm and that might hurt."

"I don't care! Do it through my arm."

It took him a few tries, but he accessed a vein in my arm, and just for a minute...I felt totally in control. I had this.

For a minute anyway.

I'M READY TO FACE 2018. ARE YOU?

The other day I was driving to UPS to pick up my business mail (yes, I'm still trying to work full-time!)...and I had a moment.

I was driving the speed limit. I wasn't in a rush and was simply taking in the trees, the big blue sky...and as I saw cars pass me, I wondered what their stories were. Where are they going? Are they hurting? Are they happy? What's their life like? Do they have cancer? You know...the questions that run through your head when you have a 'cancer' filter.

And then I realized that everyone is in such a damn RUSH!

I started sobbing and saying out loud to myself, "Why is everyone in such a hurry? Don't they know how precious this moment is? And the next?" My life has changed...I don't know if I'll ever look at life the way I did pre-cancer again.

I don't have many fond memories of 2017. Unfortunately, it ends with my being sick during the "most wonderful time of the year!"

It's hard to look forward to 2018. To be honest, I'm worried. I'm scheduled to have a double mastectomy in the spring, assuming we ever finish chemo (insert sarcasm here). Then, after I recover from surgery, I start six weeks of daily radiation. Then, after radiation, I will need to make a decision about reconstruction. Not to be confused with a 'boob job,' oh no. It's all about having skin and muscle cut from either my back, my side, or my abdomen, and then relocated to my chest so they can wrap it around an implant (just so I have some type of "form" there). Needless to say, it's the most major surgery of them all (way worse than the mastectomy). Maybe I'll just jump on the "go flat" wagon so I can avoid yet another surgery as, at this point, my medical calendar is so intense I can't even wrap my head around it.

Although thinking of 2018 right now is daunting, I suppose I am looking forward to the end of this wicked process. While the first 6-7 months will be a long, hard road, there will be a time when I have all of this behind me and am cancer free! My plan is to continue to push forward and not look back. Of course, when times are tough Mark's strength will continue to carry me forward. I look forward to this same time next year when I can look back on the madness and be thankful it's over.

(Never, ever did I think there wouldn't be a same time this year. That just wasn't a possibility. Everything we did, everything we planned, everything we focused on was all about getting me cured.)

I head back to the cancer center tomorrow—hoping I won't get turned away for my weekly chemo again. Right now, the only thing I hope and pray for is to have a strong enough body to withstand chemo so I can stay on track and move forward.

Last year, I was scoping out a new beach cruiser bicycle for the holidays. This year I hope for chemo...and to be cured.

What a difference a year makes.

How are you going to change the way you live in 2018? Will your health and wellness be your number one priority? If you can do one favor for me (it would be to please make it a priority). At the very least, I hope you "Carpe Diem" the hell out of 2018.

Happy Holidays and Happy New Year!

January, 2018

It was a strange holiday season, especially looking back knowing that, barring some sort of miracle, it will probably be my last. But I didn't feel that way then. I was still doing chemo while friends and relatives came in and out. Although looking back, it was all kind of a blur. At one point, I was experiencing hip and and back pain, and went in for an X-ray, but everything seemed fine. My CT scans were clear. My hair even started trying to grow back, like it forgot I was even on chemo at all.

In between holidays, I reflected on 2017 and what a shitshow the year had been. Things could only get better in 2018, right? 2018 was the year I was going to be cured. It was everything we were working toward.

But when I went for my first chemo treatment of the new year, I was turned away yet again. Not that it was a complete surprise. I'd been feeling really fatigued and I could feel it coming on, but I hoped I could squeak by. Turned out my counts were borderline. We thought we could push the envelope and get treatment along with some injections to boost my blood count, but the insurance company said no. So, I was delayed another week.

But January wasn't all bad news. January 9 was the very first Foye Belle Foundation event. I was there with Mark and my mom, who lives nearby, and a bunch of friends and supporters, and we all joined forces to stuff the very first blue bags with all kinds of goodies, including a personal, handwritten note in each bag encouraging the recipient to keep fighting and to know they're not alone. The support, the sweetness, the love...it was perfect.

The next day, I was denied chemo yet again. The doctors gave me a new regime—chemo every two weeks instead of weekly, with an on-body injector. If I could just hang in there for this new regime, I'd be done on Valentine's Day.

Honey, the honeymoon was going to be over.

I couldn't wait.

On January 17, I got lucky. My "neutrophil count" was supposed to be at 1.5, and I was stuck at 1.1. However, the doctors will push it and do treatment with a count as low as 1, and this time they let me in for chemo. I was so happy – who ever thought getting my body pumped full of poison could be so exciting? This particular time was actually more painful than usual, plus they changed the regime back to every two weeks and not a full dose of the drug due to my issues with being able to withstand it. They gave me my on-body injector to take home to help boost my white blood cells and keep my counts up—I had to be ridiculously careful with germs, especially with the terrible flu that was going around earlier this year. But I took those lemons and built a lemonade stand. It was all about making it to Valentine's Day, less than a month away.

Facebook, January 23, 2018

We have stacks upon stacks of Blue Bags going out today! I'm sad because so many people need them... but I'm thrilled because they will bring some "happy" to someone feeling defeated...and they will certainly make them feel a little less blue!

January 31, 2018

With just two weeks to go until my final chemo treatment, I had a lot on my mind during what was to be my second-to-last infusion of hopefully life-saving poison. I was a chemo veteran now. Most of the people who were around when I started the process had finished and moved on, hopefully to cancer-free lives.

But still, it felt like things in my world were falling into place. The Foye Belle Foundation had really taken off. Mark went on his first trip since I was diagnosed, just a quick trip to see his daughter in Chicago, and everything went great. My mom helped with me and the dogs.

And then we got the news that February 14, Valentine's Day, would in fact be my last chemo session. I looked forward to an epic day.

Then I got even better news. All along, we had been planning for a double mastectomy to remove the masses and also the lymph nodes—a double mastectomy would get rid of everything. But when I had my last mammogram during chemo, our doctor was shocked to see how much everything shrunk. She gave us the option to do a lumpectomy and lymph node removal and keep my breasts. The new plan was to go in and remove the lymph nodes and the tumor and then, after surgery, hit it hard with radiation and get those final cancer cells.

This was shocking to everyone, including the surgeon. At Stage 4, keeping all your parts is pretty unheard of. So, we all celebrated—my family, the doctor, Mark and me. It really felt like the whole nightmare was going to end... and soon.

February, 2018

Valentine's Day 2018 was probably my happiest Valentine's Day ever. After six long, painful months, I finally got to ring the bell signifying the end of chemo. It was awesome! I was ready to move on to the next phase, on the road to being CURED and done with this chapter in my life so I could get on with it already.

(After about six days of feeing like crap, of course. Chemo is still chemo, after all, even on the last day.)

Facebook, February 19, 2018

I know there are days of rest and days where we get ahead... but now more than ever - I want to soak up every moment of time and do everything and anything I can to live life more fully while helping more people. So, instead of taking today off—I've decided to focus my energy on the #bluebag movement + The Foye Belle Foundation. While I was sick last week - we received 50 more requests for blue bags and it was driving me crazy that I didn't have the energy to get them done. So, this morning I jumped into it with my mama and hubby and we're shooting to ship 50 today! Grateful to be doing this and thankful for all the love and support! Y'all rock!

And Foye Bell kept on rocking. On February 24, the work we're doing was recognized by the United States Congress! Okay, I know Congress isn't all that popular right now, but politics aside, it was still pretty neat to be recognized for our hard work at The Foye Belle Foundation. Cancer, after all, is a non-partisan issue. It doesn't care who you voted for.

But things seemed good on that front too. No more chemo treatments meant no more side effects, and by my full body scan on February 26, I was feeling great and ready for surgery. Two days later the scan results came back looking good. We scheduled surgery for March 23 and I looked forward to the new, cancer-free life that I was sure was waiting for me just around the corner—after the 6.5 months of radiation, but still…

That's around when the headaches started.

MATT GAETZ
1ˢᵗ District, Florida

ARMED SERVICES
COMMITTEE

COMMITTEE ON THE
BUDGET

COMMITTEE ON THE
JUDICIARY

Congress of the United States
House of Representatives
Washington, DC 20515

WASHINGTON OFFICE
507 CANNON HOUSE OFFICE BUILDING
WASHINGTON, DC 20515
(202) 225-4136

DISTRICT OFFICES
226 South Palafox Place
6ᵗʰ FL
PENSACOLA, FL 32502
(850) 479-1183

February 7, 2018

Chelsea Berler
174 Watercolor Way Suite 103-420
Santa Rosa Beach, Florida 32549

Dear Mrs. Berler,

It is my esteemed honor to congragulate you on your work with the Foye Belle Foundation. To help those around us while they are not in a position to help themselves, is admirable.

Thank you for your determination to help patients receive the support they deserve.

I am proud to have such a wonderful constituent in Florida's First Congressional District. I truly commend your character and work ethic and have high hopes that others will follow your lead in partaking in exemplary service acts.

Congratulations again and thank you for your loyal commitment to excellence. You have my thoughts and prayers as you continue your fight against cancer.

I offer my warmest regards and best wishes for your continued success.

If there is anything my office can do to help in your future endeavors, please do not hesitate to reach out.

Sincerely,

Matt Gaetz
Member of Congress

March 16, 2018

OMG, those headaches. They were unlike anything I'd ever experienced before. They'd come on so strong, like the worst migraine you can imagine but only lasted about five minutes. And I was getting at least 10 of them a day. It was scary. Nobody could figure out what was causing them. The doctors thought it could be stress or anxiety, but just to make sure, they did an MRI on March 6. It came back clear. Even better, my hair was growing back.

But on March 12, the pain got so bad I went to the ER, for the first time in my entire life. The pains in my head were going down my spine all the way to my tailbone. I felt like I was going crazy. No one could see anything and all my scans kept coming back fine. But my head really did hurt. I knew it did; I felt it. What was wrong with me?

The doctors gave me an MRV, which is basically an MRI that only focuses on the veins, to get a closer look inside my head. It came back clear, so the neurologist talked with my oncologist and scheduled me for a lumbar puncture. They were going through a process of elimination, and after everything else came back clear, that was the very last test they could give me to figure out what was going on—or if I really was going crazy and the pain in my head was actually "all in my head."

March 13 was my 34th birthday. Mark planned everything, including a great dinner out with all my friends, our family, and community. I wasn't feeling so well with my headaches, but it was still such a perfect night!

I also had the lumbar puncture that week, and for the first time with the headaches, it came back positive for something. But the doctors still weren't sure what it was positive for. At the time, their biggest worry was fungal meningitis, which is serious and seriously contagious, so they admitted me to the hospital where we all sat around in close quarters all day with everyone wearing masks, waiting to find out.

Mark had flown to Louisiana that day to see his son play baseball. I reached him and told him that they were admitting me to the hospital and that something might really be wrong, just as his plane arrived. He skipped the game, turned around and flew home.

He'd been at the hospital with me for about 30 minutes when the doctor came in with the results.

It wasn't meningitis.

It was much, much worse.

The breast cancer had spread to my brain fluid and my spinal fluid, not back when they tested me for brain cancer before, but probably sometime in February, according to the doctors.

And it was terminal.

Here's the official diagnosis from Medscape.com, rare as hell:

Leptomeningeal carcinomatosis (LC) is a rare complication of cancer in which the disease spreads to the membranes (meninges) surrounding the brain and spinal cord. LC occurs in approximately 5% of people with cancer and is usually terminal. If left untreated, median survival is 4-6 weeks; if treated, median survival is 2-3 months.

My mom laid down on top of me, and we cried in my hospital bed, while Mark stepped out with the doctor and talked in the hallway. He came back about an hour later. Then we all cried.

But still…I just couldn't believe it.

I never thought I wouldn't beat cancer. I thought I had it and I was good to kick its ass. NEVER did I think it would win. But cancer is kicking my ass, not the other way around. I had sworn I wouldn't let it take everything from me, in writing and everything. I shaved my own head (well, Mark did), I started a foundation, I fought with everything I had and did everything I was supposed to do.

But ultimately, it just wasn't my decision to make. Cancer is still here, it's mad and it's going to take my life.

And there's nothing, NOTHING I can do about it. No cure, no nothing.

Now I had to find a way to tell everybody.

Chapter 6

A SPRING OF TRANSITION

Facebook, March 23, 2018

March is one of my very favorite months here in Florida. I turned 34 this month so birthdays are always fun...but, mostly, it's the birds in the morning that wake me up that are an absolute joy. There's something to be said about lying in bed restlessly with the sun trying to peek in and the sound of the birds (two blue and one red one today) chirping away. They like to play in my garden in the mornings, and our master bedroom/porch is right above the garden so it's a perfect location to wake up! They sound so happy, so excited to start their day...just makes me lay here and smile. It's a good time to daydream...to take a good long look at my life, my day - this moment.

I've been contemplating this post for a few days now...wondering how to say the right thing...or help everyone understand where things are at. I'm sorry I haven't written in a while - I know you all have been asking about how I'm doing and I thank you so much for that. The first three parts to my journey are still over at the Huffington Post, but I thought I'd just stick this last update here to keep it easy...

Today is the day I was supposed to have surgery to remove my breast cancer. However, as many of you already know, it was cancelled. Last week we found out that my cancer has spread and is now in my spine and brain. A very rare disease called Leptomeningeal Carcinomatosis (LC). Right now our plan is just to keep comfortable and I'm just going to keep doing what I can until I can't. First and foremost, I don't need any sadness here, no pity, please. I'm trying hard to make our days count more than ever before... so, send your prayers, your love and your light. They will brighten our days, no doubt!

Life, such a complicated thing. It can be here one day and not the next. Never did I imagine getting a terminal diagnosis from this journey...I always thought I'd push through and come out stronger on the other side, cancer free. But, it didn't happen that way and there's nothing anyone can do about it.

So, I sit here and reflect...

I'm so damn grateful for my life. I have been so fortunate and so loved. I'm frustrated because there's so much more I want to do, to be, to love, but...it's just not in the cards. Sure, I have regrets...but mostly it's forgetting from time to time how none of this is guaranteed and we have to get out there and live more fully. Moving forward, I will focus on enjoying the time I do have as opposed to thinking about the time I will miss...

If you know my husband, our family, and friends... they could use all the support right now. Now and in the future. So, if I could make one request - it would be to not be a stranger to them and help me help them even when I'm no longer here.

I hope to see you for a bit more here on social media so I'll try and pop in from time to time, but until then... thank you for being in my life. It's better because of you. Enjoy each moment...and be kind to yourself and your surroundings. Please do that - for me.

With all my love,
Chelsea

P.S. We are working on transitioning my business, Solamar Agency, to very capable internal hands. The very same team that has been working alongside me for years...so, for any of my client friends reading this - more to come and not to worry. Also, my husband, sisters and close friends are going to continue spearheading the Blue Bag Movement over at The Foye Belle Foundation and I'm so grateful to them and all that's to come with the foundation. We have to keep pushing and supporting those in need.

P.P.S. Here are some pictures of my garden and where I spend most of my time... it's truly epic. I think one of the most peaceful things you can do is get your hands dirty in a little soil and grow something. If you don't do this, try it. For me...I consider it my meditation (I have a hard time quieting the mind :) but this process does the trick for me. It takes me to a sweet, soft, comfortable place where I feel rooted, just like the plants that stand here. One of my favorite pics is that of my hubby laying in the hammock. He doesn't slow down much, but when he does - he falls into the garden vortex too...and it's just what he needs. For now, we'll be here...see you around.

I'VE ALWAYS BEEN SURROUNDED BY LOVE.

My childhood wasn't easy—I grew up in a small town in North Dakota, surviving on food stamps and powdered milk while my mom worked three jobs trying to keep a roof over our heads and my dad was in and out of treatment centers for alcoholism. My mom tried so hard, until she finally took me and my sisters and left him when I was six.

Still, I saw him as much as I could and talked to him every day until he finally died from his disease when I was 11. It broke my heart. I loved him so much.

I also lost a half-brother and a stepbrother to car accidents before I was out of high school. So, I dealt with a lot of loss when I was really young, and I didn't always deal with it really well. At times I was kind of a mess.

But through it all, I never lacked for love. I always had my mom, my rock, who was and still is my best friend. And I had my sisters—Alicia, who is five years older than me, and Jessica, who is three years older. They gave me a lot of crap growing up (after all, I was the baby) but mostly, they were my protectors. We were always close. Really, really close. We still are today.

It was just us girls until my stepdad Bob came along and took us all in and gave us a little more stability. That's when I got my stepbrother Brady, who I also loved a lot and lost way too young.

My sisters still live in North Dakota. Alicia is a hair stylist, and really successful. She has two daughters, Kambree and Avaree, and thanks to me(!), she's married to her high school sweetheart Trevor. They were both divorced with two kids (his are Jocelyn and Karson) and I connected them via Facebook...and the rest is history. They got married and they are the BEST couple ever.

Jessica is the most educated person in our family. She owns a boutique, she's super smart and she even ran for office. She has two kids, Reed and Lola.

So that means I have four nieces and two nephews, in addition to my sisters. And Trevor.

I get to see a lot more of my mom and Bob. They moved to 30A about three years ago, and now they live right down the road from me. It's the best ever. My mom and I have a lot in common. We love gardening, plants, decorating, our homes...we love running around and just being together, eating sushi and drinking wine. She's still really involved in my life and with the Foye Belle Foundation (Foye Belle was her mother). I see her every day, and Bob too. I even FaceTime with her every single morning. We're always talking...

All these years later, I'm still surrounded by love.

I didn't tell my sisters when I first found out I had cancer. I was too busy freaking out, so that job fell to Mark. He's been "the voice" through this whole ordeal, keeping everyone in the loop on all the latest developments, and I don't envy him. It's not an easy job.

My sisters flew down after I was first diagnosed and have been coming to visit every few weeks ever since. Their support has been incredible and consistent and reliable…it's been more than I could have imagined. As horrible as this past year has been, I don't think I've ever felt more loved.

My sisters weren't with me in the hospital when I found out my cancer was terminal. Only my mom and

Mark were there when the doctor delivered the news. So once again, the job of telling them fell to Mark. And it was so hard. It still is. My mom has been communicating with them a lot too. We've all just been trying to stay connected in between their visits.

And then, there are Mark's kids. That's been a tough one too.

My stepkids, Allison and Matt, are pretty upset. And although I want to see them, I've asked them not to come. Because I don't want them to remember the way I am now (yucky). I want them to remember the way I was.

The way we were.

The thing is, I have such bad memories of my dad being ill when I was a kid. Sometimes that's all I remember, him being so rough looking. Even though I loved him, I kind of wish someone would have shielded me from it. So that's what I'm doing with Mark's kids. Although I'm heartbroken to not see them one last time, I think it's for the best, so they remember the good. Ugh, I'm hoping I'm making the right decision here. It's SO DAMN HARD. I guess there are no "right answers" in a situation like mine. But I feel like kids, even if they are in their early 20s, get so impacted by this stuff, and I don't want that to be what they remember. I want them to remember ME—not me being sick.

So, as you can probably imagine, this time with my family, with these people who I love and who love me, has been really rough. Especially with my mom. You're not supposed to outlive your youngest child; it's not fair. It's so hard on her. But she's still my rock. And we're all getting through.

We're all finding peace in it, in our own way.

April, 2018

From the time I was diagnosed with cancer, way back in September when this whole nightmare started, there was never a point where Mark and I discussed the possibility that I wouldn't survive this. We NEVER talked about it. The "d-word" was not mentioned. It wasn't something that was even on the table. We were on the path to a cure and so was the doctor—we all were. That word, terminal, it didn't feel real. It certainly didn't when I first heard it.

But within about two weeks, I started to feel it. And now, each day I decline.

We treated it in the beginning. We were doing lumbar punctures twice a week, but after a few weeks, Mark and I made a joint decision to stop. We didn't even know if the treatments were helping, I was still declining and we were getting tired of being at the doctor and doctor-ing. We wondered, why not just live our days the way we want to live them? Why not stop with the nonsense already? (Yes, somehow getting closer to death has made me sound like an old, Jewish grandma. Go figure!)

So that's what we're doing. We bought the dream car we'd been putting off until I "got better," an old Land Rover Defender, but fixed up and shiny and clean, and plan to take drives, eat ice cream and just enjoy the ride for as long as we can.

I may feel tired and slow and the feeling in my legs may be slowing going away, but I'm here and living each day the way I want to.

Beyond that, even though it's happening to me, the process of dying is still hard to describe. Each day seems a little harder than the last. I'm not sleeping well, and I'm having a hard time with things like baths, stairs, getting out of the house…and I know it will only get harder. Mentally it's even more exhausting. I've been working on getting my trust and wills in order and my business transitioned. It's really emotional. My entire family is struggling. But I guess that makes sense.

Facebook, April 16, 2018

I've watched every sunrise in the last 32 days...and it makes me wonder why I slept through them for so many years. I always thought my favorite was a big 'ol colorful sunset in the eve (don't get me wrong...those are magnificent too!)...but I realize now I've been missing the most beautiful part of the day. Tired or not folks, get up earlier, watch a few more sunrises...and carpe diem!!

It's hard, but somehow I'm at peace with dying now… and just moving along with it. At first it was shock, scary, WTF is going to happen? And honestly, when it comes to the actual act of dying, I'm still totally scared. But I did the research and the doctor has prepped us (and of course Mark asked a million questions) so I know what to expect and the process and Mark does too. I know that each day is going to be a certain way, but I'm glad to be informed, and I'm ready.

Mark's not doing as well, but I can't expect him to. He's the one being left behind, alone in the yellow house on the left with our dogs and our memories. So, we're just trying to get through, and it's been hard.

But we've had the best conversations.

Marrying a man who is 18 years older than you are comes with a few assumptions. Like that one day down the line, way, way off in the future, he's gonna get old. He's gonna need your help to get through the day and deal with the changes of growing older and ultimately leave this life behind. I knew that about Mark. I mean, he's in amazing shape now and has been as long as I've known him. But we always assumed that someday I would be Mark's caregiver.

Instead, he's mine.

Irony kind of sucks sometimes.

Our age difference came up right away, that first night together, when he whisked me away from Bud and Alley's on the back of his motorcycle and into what would be the most important relationship of my life. The night itself was amazing and such an epic night of fun. It was a beautiful ride right along the beach. We went for dinner, drinks, dancing…he was a complete gentleman. When he kissed me, he leaned me over just like in *Dirty Dancing*. It literally took my breath away.

At one point that evening we met up with some of his friends, and he turned to me and asked, with great concern, "Do you know how old I am?" I knew he was older, but he looked about 35 or 36, which was about 10 years older than me, which is pretty normal and definitely not scandalous or anything. But honestly, I didn't care. I'd been married and divorced twice, and I'd never, ever had a night like that in my life, where a man just took charge and made me feel so cared about and special. It was like a fairy tale. And, since he lived in another state and had an ex-wife and two kids, even though we exchanged phone numbers, I honestly didn't know if I'd ever even see him again.

Two weeks later, I had seen him again. And again. And it was pretty clear there were going to be a lot more agains in our future. So he brought the age thing up one more time, and this time, he dropped the bomb. He was 43.

Holy shit. That definitely was older than I expected.

But if I didn't care that first night, at that point, I REALLY didn't care. I was already smitten. I could not have cared less what he said his age was. He was SO WORRIED about it, and I was not, at all. And after that, we were like, "Screw it. It's all good. We're in love!"

My mom, on the other hand, was freaking out.

I did not have what you'd call the best track record when it came to relationships. Stability had not been my strong suit. So when I announced that I had a new boyfriend who was divorced with two teenage kids and also, by the way, biologically old enough to be my father, my mom and my entire family, thought I lost my mind. Again.

Like, "Here's another one of Chelsea's crazy moments..."

But when they met Mark, they actually REALLY liked him. And after that, they were okay with everything. I mean, they had a lot of questions for him and for me... and really, really wanted to understand what we were doing...so they were careful. And they did think it was super weird that he was that much older than me. And, okay, it did take a while before they were totally on board. But they were really great about it after they saw the man he was, how he was with me and how we were together.

How we are together.

The weird thing is, we are COMPLETE opposites. Truly. He is everything I'm not, in all the right ways. And I am everything he's not. I would say we both bring strong and soft, but in totally different manners. I think that's why it works. I'm very laid back and he's very Type A. I would describe him as a bit wound up…he stresses about EVERYTHING and is very much a perfectionist. And I'm very like, "Yeah, whatever."

Another weird thing…our personalities completely mirror our two dogs' personalities. Our two rescue dogs, Stella and Dakota (who we call Kota), are basically our kids. They're totally spoiled and pretty much the center of our lives. We love them so much, and I'm going to miss them so much! Stella is the crazy one and everyone says she's just like Mark, and Kota is the chill one that everyone says is like me. Although Stella does like to sleep in and be lazy in the mornings, and that's very much NOT Mark. But everything else about her totally is. It's kind of hilarious.

Overall, it's really just a beautiful mesh of goodness. It works so well for us. Damn, I love my husband the way he is…his crazy ways. I think he's really misunderstood by a lot of people and I just GET him. I just get it. I meet him where he needs to be met. Where he is. And that's why it works.

And why I'm so damn sad to have to leave him.

All these years together, I was SO all over knowing that one day, when he needed me, I would be able to take care of him. I knew and wanted to be the one to take good care of him as he got older. It sucks because now I'm worried about him being alone, not having me to do all that stuff… damn, it sucks.

Because I really wanted to be his person. This is what I'm good at. Taking care of others. I wanted it to be me to grow old with him and be there for him.

I hope for so much for him after I'm gone. I hope for an easier life where he can take life in a lot more. I hope he finds love again—or is open to it. To be honest, it breaks my heart to say that, damnit, because I still want it to be me…but everyone needs love in their life. EVERYONE needs someone to love.

I'm so grateful Mark has been my someone.

Now every day, after I watch the sunrise, I lay with Mark for a few hours and we talk. We've talked about what everything looks like, how we'll play it out, hospice, changing my office on the main level of our house into a room because I can't do the stairs really well. We've talked about life, love, dying…we talk about what his life will be like without me, our dogs, our home, everything. We're talking openly about all that and we're getting to a good place together, to just embrace this time for what it is and be together.

I've circled around to peace, and I'm truly at peace with death and dying. I'm going to miss everything. EVERYTHING. I'm sad that it all ends. That I'm going to miss everything. That I'm going to miss my family, my gardens, everything…but I'm okay.

My heart is okay now. We're going to be okay, and it is what it is.

I like to dream about where my soul will be dropped next. I'm a very spiritual person, and I truly believe that my soul will land somewhere epic. And I look forward to what that looks like. My dad and my brothers, I definitely think I'll see them all again and I'm so excited about that. And I'll wait for Mark, because I can't wait to see him again. I believe I'll be able to visit my family, my sisters and mom…and I will be able to be here too.

So, I'm looking forward to checking in from time to time and watching over everyone. Always and in all ways.

April 19, 2018 - 3:40am

I'm laying here and thinking about the things that are slowly happening to me…like sometimes in the middle of the night I get up on my feet and walk to the bathroom just to make sure they're still working…because I am losing feeling in my toes and lower legs. So every morning I try and stand up just to make sure I'm still feeling something.

It's a little scary just knowing that I am laying here hoping that when I do put my toes on the ground that they do work. Every morning is a little bit harder but every morning I can still feel my toes, so that's got to be good!

May 1, 2018

We started hospice yesterday. I don't need it too much right now, but I'm just trying to be as independent in the house as I can, while I can. My mind is still clear so yay for that! It's just my body that isn't working the best...

Hospice, for those of you lucky people who have not yet experienced it, is actually pretty great. By definition, it's a home providing care for the sick, especially the terminally ill. Right now, they're turning the yellow house on the left—our house—into that home for me. They came in and assessed the house and figured out what we need for me to get around and be able to shower and all that. So, I have a walker, a shower chair, a little cane and other stuff to make it easier to get around. They, a nurse and a CNA (Certified Nursing Assistant), will stop by as much or as little as we want or need them to and do whatever we want. They're available 24/7, so they can come every day or just when we let them know we need something. The two here yesterday were SO SWEET. Gotta take big hearts to do a job like hospice, you know? And they were wonderful, so I know I'm in great hands.

Of course my mom and Mark want to be the ones to help with as much of this stuff as they can, but the supplies and the help getting around the house has been epic. And if you ever find out that you need hospice, let me tell you, hospice nurses are like real-life angels. They will do anything you need or want, from helping you shower to just sitting with you and reading to you. We've been really lucky, our insurance covers it 100%--all the supplies, the help, everything. It's pretty amazing.

Beyond that, Mark's goal has been to try and get me out when I can—take a drive in our awesome new/old car, be together, whatever it takes to seize the day as much as we can. We have been trying to go for short drives each day. Today I didn't get out but yesterday we sure did—we went to the doctor, stopped by the post office and dropped off some t-shirt orders for Foye Belle. The other day we drove and got an epic Oreo blizzard (we've done that a few times!). One day we stopped for a pizza...a lot of our outings are food-related, since eating is one of the things I can still enjoy, and I plan to keep enjoying it as much as I can.

CHAPTER 7

ENDINGS...AND NEW BEGINNINGS

I t's hard, but I have come to peace with leaving. I will miss my family, friends, my dogs, my home, my garden... everything about my amazing, beautiful time here on this earth, and especially in the yellow house on the left.

While my time was shorter than I would have hoped, I feel like I have lived a fulfilling life. I cherish every moment these days and spend a lot of time thinking about what is important to leave behind, mostly when watching the sunrise each morning while listening to the birds chirping in my backyard. What I recently realized is, the exact same things I would love to leave behind are those very same things that guide my remaining days:

> There are no endings - only new beginnings
> Don't spend time worrying, the time you have is now - spend time living
> Always know there are an infinite number of beautiful experiences waiting to happen - seek them out

> Make each day count more than the previous day
> Always believe in the goodness in people
> The world is an incredible place - make the most of it
> And lastly, always take the scenic route...

With all my love, Chelsea

 "If the only prayer you ever say in your entire life is thank you, it will be enough."

—MEISTER ECKHART

CONNECT WITH CHELSEA

ON THE WEB
🖥 mostlychelsea.com

SOCIAL MEDIA
f facebook.com/mostlychelsea
📷 instagram.com/mostlychelsea

EMAIL
✉ hello@mostlychelsea.com